Mathematics Grade 2

TABLE OF CONTENTS

FRACTIONS, MEASUREMENTS & EQUATIONS

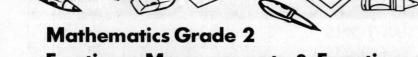

Mathematics Grade 2
Fractions, Measurements & Equations

Materials You Will Need:

❑ A good pencil (or 2) with a working eraser

❑ Crayons

❑ A ruler with inches & centimeters

Check your work with the Answer Key at the back of this book!

Benefits of Math Grade 2 –
Fractions, Measurements & Equations:

1. Comparing Numbers will be easy!

2. Wow your friends by solving 2-Digit & 3-Digit Addition & Subtraction equations!

3. You'll be able to measure length, weight & capacity!

4. Spend money & pass the time like a pro!

5. You can master beginning in Multiplication!

Parent & Teacher Coaching Tips:

❑ *Prepare.* Provide your child with a quiet, well-lit place to study. Prepare a desk or table with an upright chair that is comfortable. Make sure that your child has plenty of room to work & spread out materials.

❑ *Schedule.* Set a study schedule. Choose a time that seems to work well for your child. Include your child in this study scheduling process and select a time when your child is well-rested and alert. Be sure to allow a break from working after a long school day.

❑ *Engage.* How does your child learn best? Use your child's learning strengths to reinforce information AND work on building new skills with your child. Encourage FUN through movement, play, acting, writing, drawing, singing, music, talking, thinking, and more while you work with your child.

❑ *Break.* Take frequent breaks from studying. Throughout the book, you will find review pages after each section of skills. When your child completes the section, use the book mark to mark your place in the book. Take a break and return to studying at your next scheduled time.

❑ *Relax!* Your role is critical in helping your child succeed with this workbook, at school, and with standardized tests. Be sure to help your child to: eat well, sleep well, practice deep-breathing techniques to relax, visualize success, and release energy in a physical way (running, walking, playing sports).

❑ *Talk.* Encourage your child to talk about feelings related to test-anxiety, help your child understand the need for tests AND stress the value of <u>real</u> learning that is not always obvious with test scores.

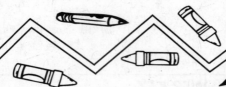

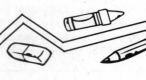

Name:_____ Date:_____

Color the boxes from **75** to **100**, in order,
to make a path from Start to Finish.

Start

75	76	77	80	81	93	94
78	71	78	79	91	80	83
72	89	79	83	93	94	95
82	81	80	88	92	91	96
83	88	79	72	91	98	97
84	76	75	78	90	92	98
85	86	87	88	89	93	99
88	92	94	93	91	87	100

Finish

Name:_____   Date:_____

Find the pattern. Write the missing numbers.

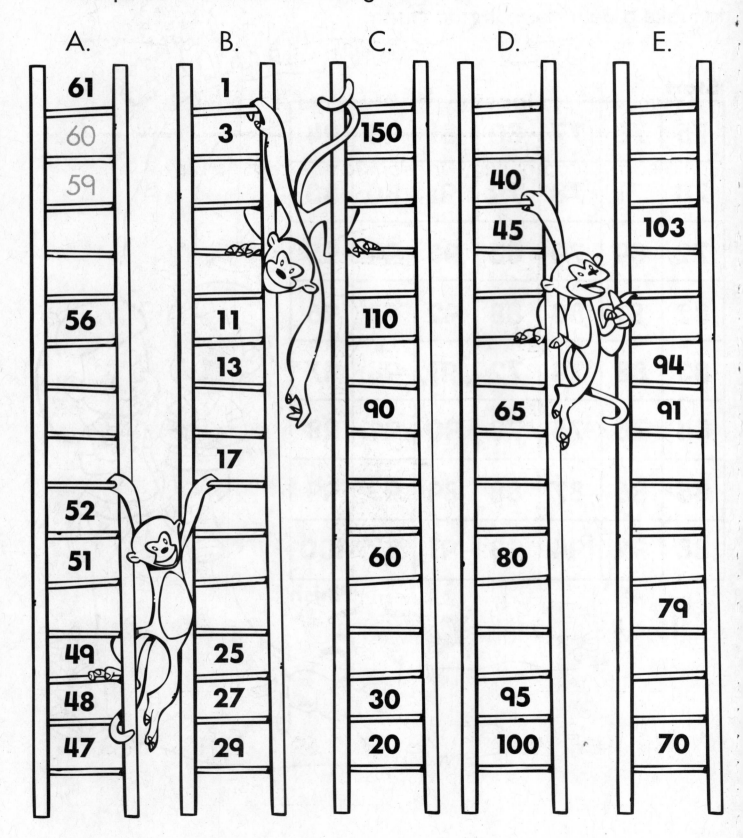

A.	B.	C.	D.	E.
61	1		40	
60	3	150	45	
59				103
56	11	110		94
	13		65	91
52	17	90		
51		60	80	
				79
49	25			
48	27	30	95	
47	29	20	100	70

Identifying and continuing number patterns

Name:_____ Date:_____

The numbers from **least** to **greatest** are 45, 54, 60.

Write each group of numbers from **least** to **greatest**.

A. **10   30   20**   **75   57   68**
   10   20   30
   ___ ___ ___   ___ ___ ___

B. **18   23   14**   **35   27   31**

   ___ ___ ___   ___ ___ ___

C. **45   48   52**   **67   82   53**

   ___ ___ ___   ___ ___ ___

D. **34   41   29**   **60   47   59**   **90   68   77**

   ___ ___ ___   ___ ___ ___   ___ ___ ___

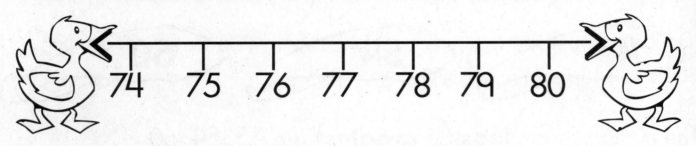

< means "is less than"
76 < 78

> means "is greater than"
77 > 75

Complete each sentence by adding < or >.
Be sure the duck's mouth is open to the greater number.

A.
| 20 > 19 | 36   40 | 18   81 |

B.
| 80   68 | 54   34 | 16   71 |

C.
| 36   39 | 25   29 | 50   49 |

D.
| 27   72 | 82   85 | 71   79 |

E.
| 60   59 | 30   39 | 48   50 |

F.
| 39   31 | 56   85 | 19   21 |

Name:_____ Date:_____

Draw lines to match the numbers to the correct number words and place value descriptions.

8 tens and 3 ones   97   fifty-eight

5 tens and 8 ones   58   forty-three

3 tens and 1 one   43   ninety-seven

9 tens and 7 ones   26   eighty-nine

8 tens and 9 ones   64   sixty-four

7 tens and 5 ones   83   twenty-six

6 tens and 4 ones   75   thirty-one

2 tens and 6 ones   89   seventeen

1 ten and 7 ones   31   eighty-three

4 tens and 3 ones   17   seventy-five

Odd numbers end in 1, 3, 5, 7, and 9.
Even numbers end in 0, 2, 4, 6, and 8.

Color treasures with **odd** numbers [blue] .
Color treasures with **even** numbers [yellow] .

Challenge: Draw more treasures in the picture. Label them with **even** or **odd** numbers. Then, color them according to the **even-odd** color code.

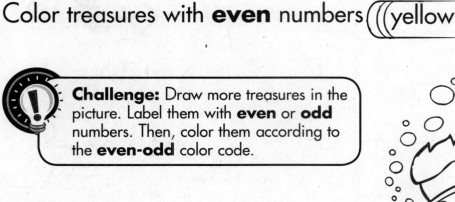

39 31

29 24

91 7

86 34 16
75 49 96

47

72 84 18

43 44

Name:_____   Date:_____

Review: Number Patterns

Find each pattern. Write the missing numbers.

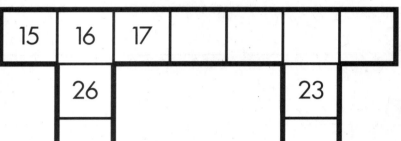

| 15 | 16 | 17 | | | | |

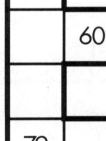

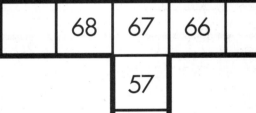

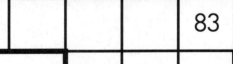

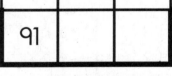

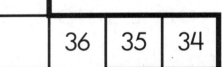

Name:_____ Date:_____

Review: Comparing Numbers

Write the numbers in reverse order from **greatest** to **least**.

A. 56   77   68   ____ ____ ____

B. 312   123   231   ____ ____ ____

C. 743   634   467   ____ ____ ____

D. 190   214   349   ____ ____ ____

E. 43   41   48   ____ ____ ____

F. 497   528   479   ____ ____ ____

Compare each pair of numbers. Complete each sentence by adding < or >.

G. 86 □ 44	35 □ 76	89 □ 98	53 □ 61
H. 27 □ 16	41 □ 56	37 □ 51	67 □ 24

STOP! TAKE A BREAK! You did a great job! Place your Book Mark here & RELAX!

Add.

$9 + 9 =$ _____ 18

Tip:
Draw the number of golf balls in each equation, and count them to help you solve each problem.

$9 + 7 =$ _____

A. $10 + 2 =$ _____ $4 + 6 =$ _____ $10 + 8 =$ _____

B. $8 + 9 =$ _____ $7 + 9 =$ _____ $9 + 6 =$ _____

C. $8 + 8 =$ _____ $7 + 3 =$ _____ $0 + 7 =$ _____

D. $2 + 6 =$ _____ $8 + 0 =$ _____ $6 + 3 =$ _____

E. $5 + 8 =$ _____ $6 + 6 =$ _____ $9 + 2 =$ _____

$$7 + 4 = 11$$

Write the missing number inside the paw for each equation.

A.

$$\begin{array}{r} 6 \\ + \\ \hline 14 \end{array}$$

$$\begin{array}{r} \\ + 9 \\ \hline 12 \end{array}$$

$$\begin{array}{r} 8 \\ + \\ \hline 13 \end{array}$$

$$\begin{array}{r} \\ + 9 \\ \hline 17 \end{array}$$

B.

$$\begin{array}{r} \\ + 8 \\ \hline 16 \end{array}$$

$$\begin{array}{r} \\ + 7 \\ \hline 7 \end{array}$$

$$\begin{array}{r} 9 \\ + \\ \hline 18 \end{array}$$

$$\begin{array}{r} 10 \\ + \\ \hline 13 \end{array}$$

C.

$$\begin{array}{r} 3 \\ + \\ \hline 11 \end{array}$$

$$\begin{array}{r} \\ + 7 \\ \hline 15 \end{array}$$

$$\begin{array}{r} 5 \\ + \\ \hline 15 \end{array}$$

Name:_____   Date:_____

Cross out and subtract.

A.

$$11 - 5 = \underline{6}$$

B.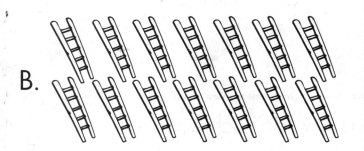

$$14 - 6 = \underline{\hspace{2cm}}$$

C.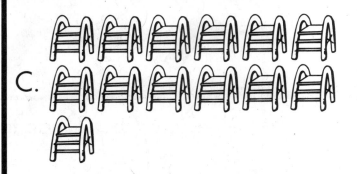

$$13 - 4 = \underline{\hspace{2cm}}$$

Subtract.

D. $15 - 7 = \underline{\hspace{1.5cm}}$ $18 - 9 = \underline{\hspace{1.5cm}}$ $17 - 9 = \underline{\hspace{1.5cm}}$

E. $11 - 3 = \underline{\hspace{1.5cm}}$ $16 - 8 = \underline{\hspace{1.5cm}}$ $10 - 6 = \underline{\hspace{1.5cm}}$

F. $14 - 9 = \underline{\hspace{1.5cm}}$ $15 - 9 = \underline{\hspace{1.5cm}}$ $12 - 7 = \underline{\hspace{1.5cm}}$

G. $12 - 4 = \underline{\hspace{1.5cm}}$ $8 - 2 = \underline{\hspace{1.5cm}}$ $9 - 8 = \underline{\hspace{1.5cm}}$

Write the missing number inside each magnifying glass.

A.

14
− ___
6

12
− ___
9

− 5
7

10
− ___
7

B.

− 8
8

18
− ___
9

13
− ___
6

− 4
8

C.

17
− ___
8

− 7
4

14
− ___
9

9
− ___
5

D.

− 6
3

Tip:
Subtraction is the opposite of addition. The two smaller numbers added together will give you the larger number.

Front-end estimation is a quick way to find an approximate sum total.

2-digit equations: Add the digits in the tens place; drop down a zero in the ones place.

3-digit equations: Add the digits in the hundreds place; drop down a zero in the tens place and the ones place.

$$\begin{array}{r} 52 \\ + 22 \\ \hline \end{array} \quad \begin{array}{r} 50 \\ + 20 \\ \hline 70 \end{array}$$

$$\begin{array}{r} 621 \\ + 302 \\ \hline \end{array} \quad \begin{array}{r} 600 \\ + 300 \\ \hline 900 \end{array}$$

Find an approximate sum total using **front-end estimation**.

A.
$$\begin{array}{r} 34 \\ + 43 \\ \hline \end{array} \quad +$$

$$\begin{array}{r} 62 \\ + 34 \\ \hline \end{array} \quad +$$

$$\begin{array}{r} 83 \\ + 33 \\ \hline \end{array} \quad +$$

B.
$$\begin{array}{r} 94 \\ + 22 \\ \hline \end{array} \quad +$$

$$\begin{array}{r} 54 \\ + 51 \\ \hline \end{array} \quad +$$

$$\begin{array}{r} 64 \\ + 23 \\ \hline \end{array} \quad +$$

C.
$$\begin{array}{r} 634 \\ + 243 \\ \hline \end{array} \quad +$$

$$\begin{array}{r} 516 \\ + 429 \\ \hline \end{array} \quad +$$

$$\begin{array}{r} 847 \\ + 625 \\ \hline \end{array} \quad +$$

Front-end estimation is a quick way to find an approximate difference.

 Challenge: After finding an approximate difference with front-end estimation, solve each equation to find the *actual* difference. How close are the estimate and actual sums?

Find an approximate difference using **front-end estimation**.

A.
44
− 33 −

84
− 33 −

92
− 51 −

B.
64
− 42 −

71
− 25 −

54
− 43 −

C.
934
− 443 −

844
− 527 −

625
− 309 −

Name: _____ Date: _____

Review: Addition & Subtraction

Write in the missing sign **+** or **–** for each equation.

A. $5 \,\square\, 3 = 8$ $4 \,\square\, 1 = 3$ $9 \,\square\, 4 = 5$

B. $7 \,\square\, 2 = 5$ $3 \,\square\, 3 = 6$ $3 \,\square\, 2 = 1$

C. $1 \,\square\, 6 = 7$ $4 \,\square\, 4 = 0$ $8 \,\square\, 6 = 2$

D. $12 \,\square\, 5 = 7$ $9 \,\square\, 2 = 11$ $18 \,\square\, 9 = 9$

E. $8 \,\square\, 6 = 14$ $13 \,\square\, 4 = 9$ $16 \,\square\, 8 = 8$

F. $8 \,\square\, 9 = 17$ $5 \,\square\, 3 = 2$ $8 \,\square\, 1 = 9$

G. $10 \,\square\, 5 = 5$ $15 \,\square\, 8 = 7$ $6 \,\square\, 6 = 12$

H. $14 \,\square\, 2 = 16$ $4 \,\square\, 8 = 12$ $11 \,\square\, 5 = 6$

I. $9 \,\square\, 3 = 12$ $17 \,\square\, 6 = 11$ $8 \,\square\, 2 = 10$

Name:_____   Date:_____

Review: Front-End Estimation

Find an approximate sum or difference using **front-end estimation**.

A.   934   ☐   85   ☐   927   ☐

   + 443 + ☐   – 44 – ☐   + 334 + ☐

           ☐   ☐   ☐

B.   74   ☐   91   ☐   62   ☐

   – 47 – ☐   – 32 – ☐   + 81 + ☐

           ☐   ☐   ☐

C.   321   ☐   844   ☐   629   ☐

   + 443 + ☐   – 723 – ☐   + 403 + ☐

            ☐   ☐   ☐

STOP! TAKE A BREAK! You did a great job! Place your Book Mark here & RELAX!

Name: _____ Date: _____

tens	ones
2	7
+ 3	5

Add the ones.
7 ones + 5 ones
= 12 ones

tens	ones
1	
2	7
+ 3	5
	2

Regroup 12 ones as
1 ten and 2 ones.

tens	ones
1	
2	7
+ 3	5
6	2

Add the tens.
1 ten + 2 tens + 3 tens
= 6 tens

Write the sum. Circle it if you regrouped.

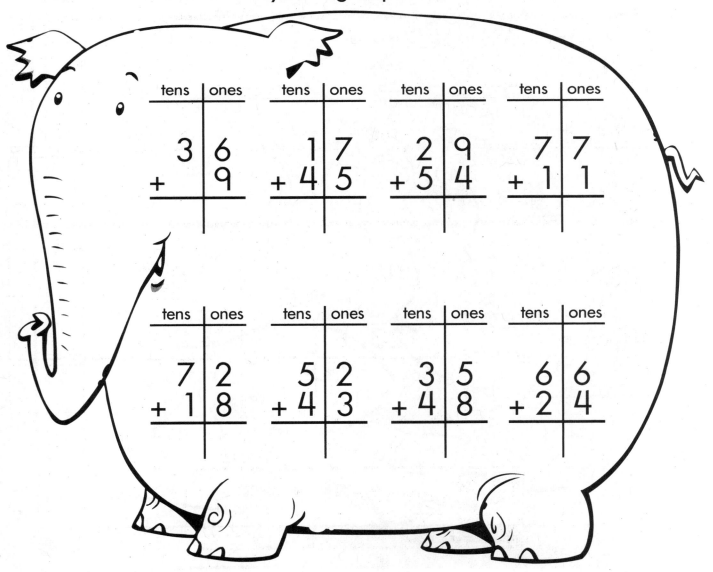

tens	ones
3	6
+	9

tens	ones
1	7
+ 4	5

tens	ones
2	9
+ 5	4

tens	ones
7	7
+ 1	1

tens	ones
7	2
+ 1	8

tens	ones
5	2
+ 4	3

tens	ones
3	5
+ 4	8

tens	ones
6	6
+ 2	4

Add to find the sum or answer. Then, use the code to color the picture.

If the sum is between	40-54	55-69	70-84	85-99
Color the creature	red	orange	green	yellow

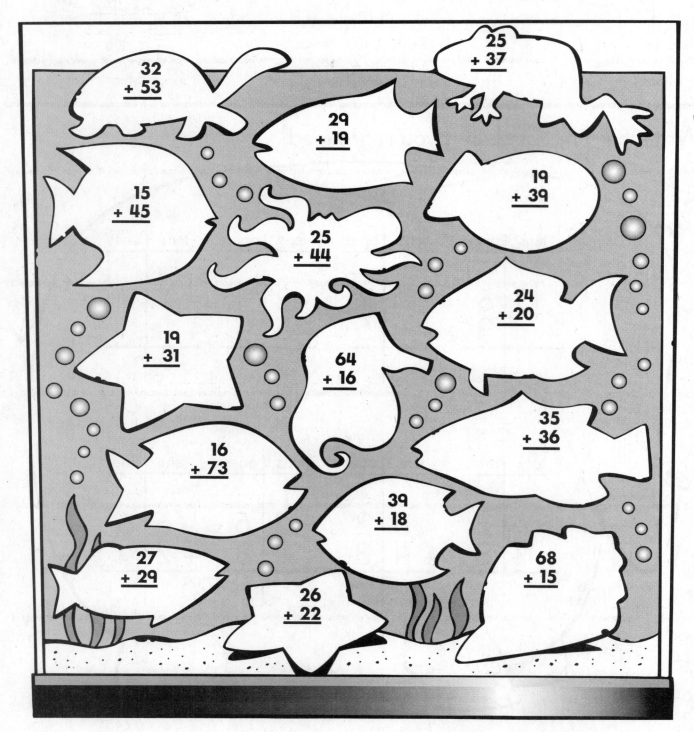

Adding 2-digit numbers with and without regrouping

Name:_____ Date:_____

Write how many hundreds, tens, and ones. Then, write the number.

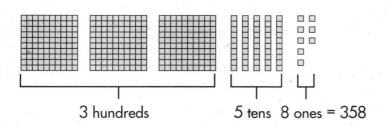 

3 hundreds   5 tens 8 ones = 358

A.

number: _____

_____ hundreds _____ tens _____ ones

B.

number: _____

_____ hundreds _____ tens _____ ones

C.

number: _____

_____ hundreds _____ tens _____ ones

D.

number: _____

_____ hundreds _____ tens _____ ones

E.

number: _____

_____ hundreds _____ tens _____ ones

F.

number: _____

_____ hundreds _____ tens _____ ones

hundreds	tens	ones
1	4	7
+ 5	3	2
		9

Add the ones.
7 ones + 2 ones = 9 ones

hundreds	tens	ones
1	4	7
+ 5	3	2
	7	9

Add the tens.
4 tens + 3 tens = 7 tens

hundreds	tens	ones
1	4	7
+ 5	3	2
6	7	9

Add the hundreds.
1 hundred + 5 hundreds = 6 hundreds.
The sum is 679.

First, add the ones. Then, add the tens. Then, add the hundreds.

A.

hundreds	tens	ones
5	1	6
+ 2	8	0

hundreds	tens	ones
3	4	0
+ 5	1	8

hundreds	tens	ones
9	4	1
+	2	8

B.

hundreds	tens	ones
3	2	6
+ 4	5	3

hundreds	tens	ones
4	3	6
+ 5	3	0

hundreds	tens	ones
8	2	1
+ 1	6	3

C.

hundreds	tens	ones
8	3	4
+	5	4

hundreds	tens	ones
1	5	2
+ 7	4	2

hundreds	tens	ones
6	0	7
+ 2	5	1

hundreds	tens	ones
	1	
2	5	8
+ 3	9	4
		2

Add the ones.
There are 12 ones.
Regroup 10 ones for
1 ten.

hundreds	tens	ones
1	1	
2	5	8
+ 3	9	4
	5	2

Add the tens.
There are 15 tens.
Regroup 10 tens for
1 hundred.

hundreds	tens	ones
1	1	
2	5	8
+ 3	9	4
6	5	2

Add the hundreds.
There are 6 hundreds.
The sum is 652.

Add. Use the example above to help you.

A.

hundreds	tens	ones
4	3	2
+ 2	8	3

hundreds	tens	ones
2	4	8
+ 3	4	6

hundreds	tens	ones
2	5	6
+ 3	3	3

B.

hundreds	tens	ones
3	6	5
+ 3	7	9

hundreds	tens	ones
1	2	5
+	4	9

C.

hundreds	tens	ones
7	8	4
+ 1	6	5

Read each story problem. Write a number sentence and solve.

1. One day, Mr. Perez sells 132 puffy animal stickers and 257 plain animal stickers. How many animal stickers did he sell that day?

_____

2. Mr. Perez ordered 527 new shiny stickers and 268 new puffy stickers. How many new stickers did Mr. Perez order?

_____

3. Ms. Ross bought 87 car stickers and 125 happy face stickers. How many stickers did Ms. Ross buy?

_____

4. Julie's scout troop bought 328 puffy stickers and 480 shiny stickers. How many stickers did the troop buy?

_____

5. Mrs. Patel bought 249 "Good Work" stickers and 518 star stickers. How many stickers did Mrs. Patel buy?

_____

6. The Sticker Club bought 375 animal stickers and 297 puffy stickers. How many stickers did the club buy?

_____

Name:_____   Date:_____

Review: 2- & 3-Digit Addition

Write each sum.

A.
$$54 + 36$$ $$39 + 52$$ $$28 + 44$$ $$51 + 29$$ $$46 + 25$$

B.
$$63 + 24$$ $$50 + 75$$ $$84 + 11$$ $$89 + 7$$ $$16 + 67$$

C.
$$236 + 143$$ $$310 + 425$$ $$200 + 354$$ $$738 + 290$$ $$359 + 427$$

D.
$$563 + 167$$ $$704 + 298$$ $$353 + 194$$ $$624 + 319$$ $$168 + 586$$

Read each story problem. Write a number sentence and solve.

1. At a garage sale, Arta's family sold 197 paperback books and 84 hardback books. How many books did they sell in all?

_____

2. Mr. Green's class read 243 books in April and 328 books in May. How many books did they read in the two-month period?

_____

Name:_____   Date:_____

Review: 2- & 3-Digit Addition

Add. Circle the sums that are greater than 599.
What pattern do you see?

A.   200   279   412   342   168
   + 400   + 110   + 213   + 247   + 321
   _____   _____   _____   _____   _____
    (600)

B.   240   353   152   412   253
   + 410   + 322   + 345   + 87   + 243

C.   509   400   620   321   230
   + 50   + 300   + 105   + 123   + 520

D.   327   316   443   400   258
   + 261   + 282   + 332   + 400   + 341

E.   622   313   500   674   600
   + 203   + 130   + 350   + 201   + 300

STOP! TAKE A BREAK! You did a great job!
Place your Book Mark here & RELAX!

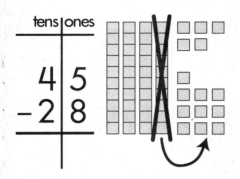

tens	ones
4	5
−2	8

You cannot subtract 8 ones
from 5 ones.
Regroup 1 ten for 10 ones.

tens	ones
3	15
4	5
−2	8
	7

Subtract the ones.
15 ones − 8 ones = 7 ones

tens	ones
3	15
4	5
−2	8
1	7

Subtract the tens.
3 tens − 2 tens = 1 ten
45 − 28 = 17

Write the difference. Circle it if you regrouped.

A.

tens	ones
3	6
−	9

tens	ones
6	8
−4	5

tens	ones
7	2
−5	4

tens	ones
5	7
−1	8

B.

tens	ones
3	2
−1	8

tens	ones
5	2
−4	7

tens	ones
9	8
−4	8

tens	ones
6	0
−2	4

Name:_____ Date:_____

Circle the greater score. Then, subtract to find the difference between the two scores.

Tip:
Be careful to line up the ones and tens columns when rewriting the problems.

A.

HOME (52)
VISITOR 49
3

HOME 63
VISITOR 51

HOME 64
VISITOR 54

B.

HOME 75
VISITOR 61

HOME 70
VISITOR 54

HOME 72
VISITOR 56

C.
HOME 84
VISITOR 78

HOME 60
VISITOR 49

HOME 90
VISITOR 83

D.
HOME 94
VISITOR 79

HOME 83
VISITOR 67

HOME 78
VISITOR 76

28   Subtracting 2-digit numbers with and without regrouping

Name:_____ Date:_____

hundreds	tens	ones
8	4	9
− 5	1	2
		7

Subtract the ones.
9 ones − 2 ones = 7 ones

hundreds	tens	ones
8	4	9
− 5	1	2
	3	7

Subtract the tens.
4 tens − 1 ten = 3 tens

hundreds	tens	ones
8	4	9
− 5	1	2
3	3	7

Subtract the hundreds.
8 hundreds − 5 hundreds =
3 hundreds
The difference is 337.

Subtract.

hundreds	tens	ones
9	7	6
− 3	5	3

hundreds	tens	ones
7	8	5
− 4	8	1

hundreds	tens	ones
5	8	6
− 2	5	4

hundreds	tens	ones
8	3	6
− 5	2	0

hundreds	tens	ones
4	9	8
− 2	5	1

hundreds	tens	ones
3	9	2
−	9	2

hundreds	tens	ones
7	3	9
− 4	5	3
		6

Subtract the ones.
9 ones − 3 ones = 6 ones

hundreds	tens	ones
6	13	
7	3	9
− 4	5	3
	8	6

You cannot subtract 5 tens
from 3 tens. Regroup
1 hundred for 10 tens.
Subtract the tens.
13 tens − 5 tens = 8 tens

hundreds	tens	ones
6	13	
7	3	9
− 4	5	3
2	8	6

Subtract the hundreds.
6 hundreds − 4 hundreds =
2 hundreds.
The difference is 286.

Subtract. Regroup if you need to.

A.

hundreds	tens	ones
5	3	9
− 1	8	7

hundreds	tens	ones
7	5	2
− 3	4	6

hundreds	tens	ones
6	4	6
− 5	3	3

B.

hundreds	tens	ones
8	6	5
− 3	7	1

hundreds	tens	ones
7	9	7
− 6	4	7

hundreds	tens	ones
6	8	4
− 1	6	5

Name:_____   Date:_____

Subtract from top to bottom. Use the answer you write in the box as the top number for the equation below it.

A.　54　　B.　67　　C.　23　　D.　48　　E.　39
　－ 13　　　－ 22　　　－ 13　　　－ 17　　　－ 10
　[ ]　　　　[ ]　　　　[ ]　　　　[ ]　　　　[ ]

　－ 20　　　－ 25　　　－ 6　　　－ 20　　　－ 7
　[ ]　　　　[ ]　　　　[ ]　　　　[ ]　　　　[ ]

　－ 11　　　－ 10　　　－ 3　　　－ 7　　　－ 11
　[ ]　　　　[ ]　　　　[ ]　　　　[ ]　　　　[ ]

F.　88　　G.　72　　H.　99　　I.　57　　J.　64
　－ 24　　　－ 31　　　－ 35　　　－ 10　　　－ 13
　[ ]　　　　[ ]　　　　[ ]　　　　[ ]　　　　[ ]

　－ 30　　　－ 20　　　－ 13　　　－ 15　　　－ 31
　[ ]　　　　[ ]　　　　[ ]　　　　[ ]　　　　[ ]

　－ 12　　　－ 11　　　－ 20　　　－ 10　　　－ 10
　[ ]　　　　[ ]　　　　[ ]　　　　[ ]　　　　[ ]

　－ 20　　　－ 6　　　－ 21　　　－ 22　　　－ 7
　[ ]　　　　[ ]　　　　[ ]　　　　[ ]　　　　[ ]

Read each story problem. Write a number sentence and solve.

1. There are 387 boys and 410 girls at the *Stars* game. How many more girls than boys are at the game?

_____

2. There are 797 children and 912 adults at the *Stars* game. How many more adults than children are at the game?

_____

3. Manny sells 425 sodas and 670 bottled waters. How many more bottled waters than sodas are sold?

_____

4. Jane sells 459 bags of peanuts and 953 hot dogs. How many more hot dogs than peanuts are sold?

_____

5. The *Stars* sell 564 pennants. Of those, 181 are small pennants and the rest are large pennants. How many large pennants are sold?

_____

6. The *Stars* give away 175 t-shirts. All but 38 of them are given to children. How many t-shirts are given to children?

_____

7. Mr. Patel has 800 *Stars* baseball caps to sell. He sells all but 282 of them. How many caps does Mr. Patel sell?

_____

8. The *Stars* play 65 games at home out of a total of 123 games. How many games are played away from home?

_____

Name:_____ Date:_____

Review: 2- & 3-Digit Subtraction

Subtract.

A.	64 − 37	89 − 54	98 − 39	41 − 27	76 − 55
B.	61 − 54	50 − 36	31 − 17	73 − 55	90 − 67
C.	70 − 53	99 − 69	36 − 25	57 − 43	61 − 33
D.	336 − 143	425 − 370	863 − 354	738 − 390	559 − 427
E.	463 − 127	764 − 228	375 − 194	624 − 319	968 − 586
F.	470 − 253	833 − 641	683 − 542	549 − 432	397 − 183

Name:_____   Date:_____

Review: 2- & 3-Digit Subtraction

Read each story problem. Write a number sentence and solve.

1. Marcia has 48 dolls and 75 stuffed animals. What is the difference between the number of stuffed animals and dolls that Marcia owns?

   _____

2. A total of 614 tickets are sold for the school play. Of those, 341 are student tickets. How many tickets are <u>not</u> student tickets?

   _____

3. There are a total of 98 rides at Jack's favorite amusement park. On one day, he rode 72 rides. How many more rides does Jack need to try?

   _____

4. The baseball field was giving out free baseballs for the first 250 fans who came through the doors. On one day, 978 fans came to the game. How many fans missed out on the free baseballs?

   _____

5. Of the 405 cars on the lot at the car dealership, 101 are black. How many cars are a color other than black?

   _____

6. Jonas has 22 play airplanes and 76 matchbox cars. What is the difference between the number of airplanes and cars that Jonas owns?

   _____

7. Julia was making bracelets for her friends. She had a bag of 242 beads to use. When she was done, she had used 116 beads. How many beads were left in the bag?

   _____

8. Of the 32 people invited to Tracy's party, 13 of them could not come. How many people attended Tracy's party?

   _____

STOP! TAKE A BREAK! You did a great job! Place your Book Mark here & RELAX!

Name:_____   Date:_____

Use an **inch** ruler to measure the path on the map. Record your answers below.

How long is the path:

1. From the entrance to the monkey?   _____ inch(es)

2. From the entrance to the snake?   _____ inch(es)

3. From the monkey to the pelican?   _____ inch(es)

4. From the snack bar to the seal?   _____ inch(es)

5. From the elephant to the lion?   _____ inch(es)

6. From the lion to the snake?   _____ inch(es)

Use a **centimeter** ruler to measure the length of each sneaker.
Sam's sneaker is 9 **centimeters** long. Find and color Sam's sneaker.

A.

____5____ centimeters

B.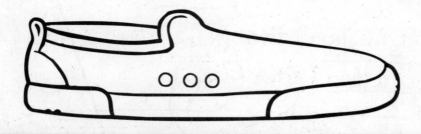

_____ centimeters

C.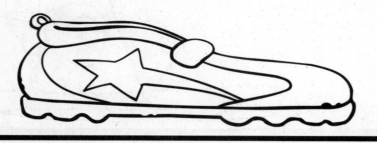

_____ centimeters

D.

_____ centimeters

E.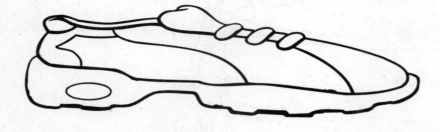

_____ centimeters

less than **1 liter**   **1 liter**   more than **1 liter**

Color the things that hold more than **1 liter** red .
Color the things that hold less than **1 liter** yellow .

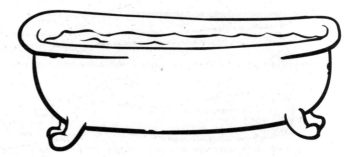

Challenge: Find examples of items that are measured in liters on your next trip to the store.

 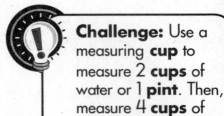

1 cup   **2 cups = 1 pint**   **4 cups = 1 quart**

Color the **cups** to show the same amounts.

 =

 =

 =

 =

 =

Comparing the capacity of cups, pints, and quarts

Name:_____   Date:_____

This spaghetti weighs 1 **pound**.
Another way to write **pound** is **lb**.

Color the things that weigh more than 1 **pound** (red).
Color the things that weigh less than 1 **pound** (blue).

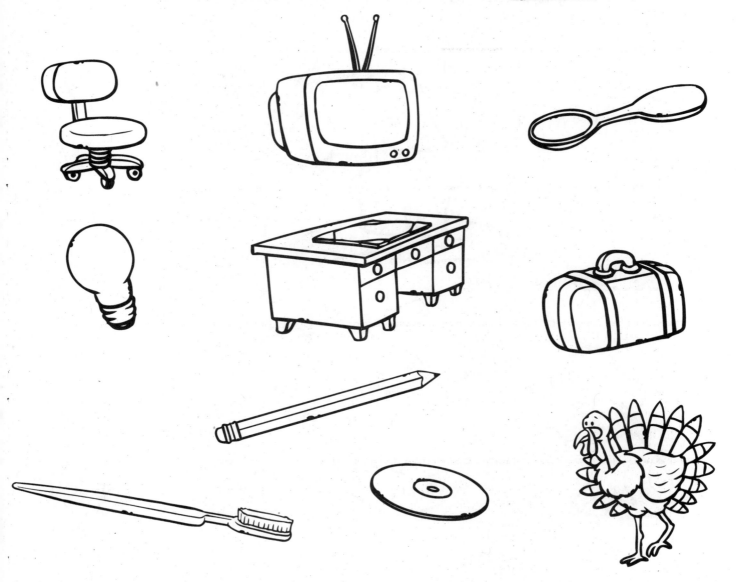

Another way to write **kilogram** is **kg**.

less than
1 kilogram

about
1 kilogram

more than
1 kilogram

Color the things that are more than **1 kilogram** (green).
Color the things that are less than **1 kilogram** (orange).

Equivalent measurements are equal in amount.

1 inch = the height of a mushroom

1 kilogram = the weight of a sack of potatoes

Look at each measurement below. Draw a picture of an object that would have roughly the **equivalent** measurement.

1 cup	1 pound	2 liters
1 foot	1 meter	1 quart

Circle the correct **temperature**.

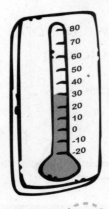 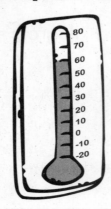

20°   30°   60°   80°

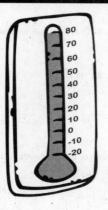 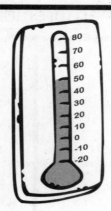

70°   80°   50°   60°

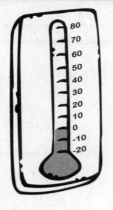 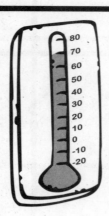

0°   10°   60°   70°

Write the **temperature**.

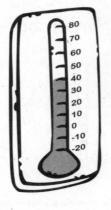 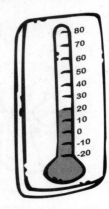

_____ °   _____ °

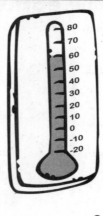 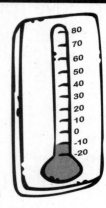

_____ °   _____ °

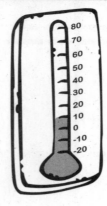 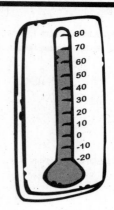

_____ °   _____ °

 Challenge: What is the **temperature** outside right now? Draw a thermometer and color it to show the **temperature** in degrees Fahrenheit.

Name:_____   Date:_____

Review: Measurement

Circle the correct answer.

1.

A 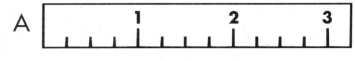 can measure _____.

                      inches   pounds

2.

2 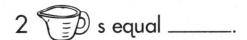 s equal _____.

3.

This 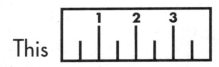 can measure _____.   kilograms   centimeters

4.

A  weighs _____.

              more than   less than

5.

A equals _____.

6.

              less than   more than

A  is _____.

Name:_____   Date:_____

Review: Measurement

Do a little research to find the measurements below. Write your approximate answers on each line.

1. Your weight: _____ pounds = _____ kilograms.

2. The height of your television: _____ centimeters.

3. The length of your shoe in inches: _____ .

4. A 16 ounce bag of licorice = _____ pound(s).

5. A 1 gallon jug of milk = _____ quart(s).

6. 4 cups of chocolate pudding = _____ quart(s).

7. 2 pints of fresh strawberries = _____ cup(s).

8. A sunflower that is 3 feet tall = _____ inches.

9. 2 quarts of lemonade = _____ pint(s).

10. 1 liter of fizzy cola = _____ milliliter(s).

11. 1,000 grams of flour = _____ kilogram(s).

Tip:
Use the conversion chart in the back of a dictionary or use the Internet to help find the measurements.

Similar shapes have the same shape, but are different in size.

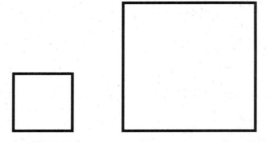

Color 3 shapes that are **similar** in each row.

A.
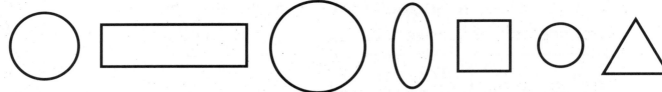

B.
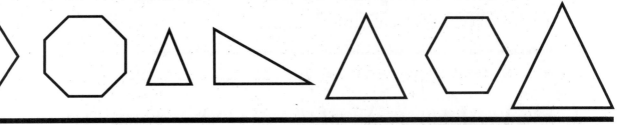

C.
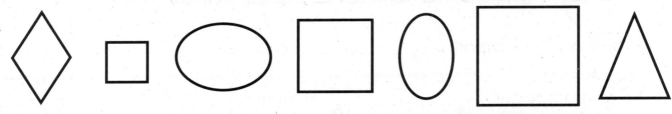

1. Draw two **similar** shapes.

2. Draw three **similar** shapes.

Congruent shapes are the same shape and size. The shape can be flipped or rotated, but it is still the same shape and size.

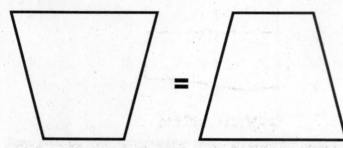 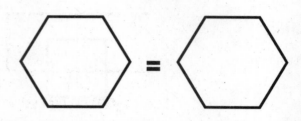

In each row, color the shapes that are **congruent**.

A.

   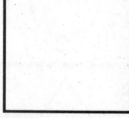

B.

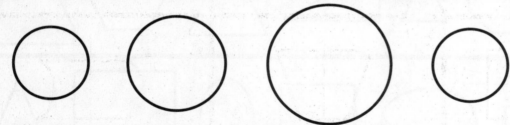

C.

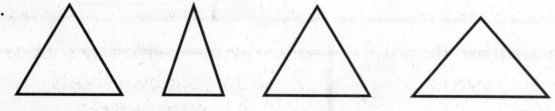

D.

A shape has **symmetry** when a line creates 2 mirror-like halves or sides that are exactly the same.

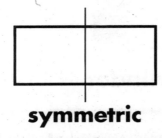

symmetric

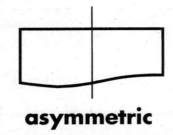

asymmetric

Look at the shapes below. Circle the correct answer.

A.

symmetric   asymmetric

B.

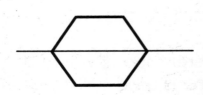

symmetric   asymmetric

C.

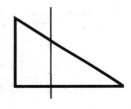

symmetric   asymmetric

D.

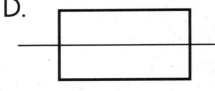

symmetric   asymmetric

E.

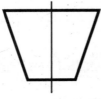

symmetric   asymmetric

F.

symmetric   asymmetric

1. Draw a line of **symmetry** on this shape.

2. Draw your own shape that is **symmetric**.

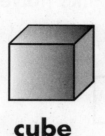      

cube   **cone**   **cylinder**   **sphere**

1. Write down 3 things that have the same shape as a **cube**.

   1. _____

   2. _____

   3. _____

 Challenge: Find some scrap paper and a roll of tape. Can you fold, bend, roll, or twist the paper to form a **cube**? How about a **cone**? Try making a **cylinder** or **sphere** with paper, too!

2. Write the name of 6 different sports where a ball shaped like a **sphere** is used.

   1. _____   4. _____

   2. _____   5. _____

   3. _____   6. _____

3. Draw a picture of 3 food products that might be found in a can shaped like a **cylinder**.

4. Draw a picture of 2 things that have the same shape as a **cone**.

Name:_____ Date:_____

Review: Similar & Congruent Shapes

Look at each pair of shapes. Color the shapes that are **similar**.
Draw an X on the box if the shapes are **not similar**.

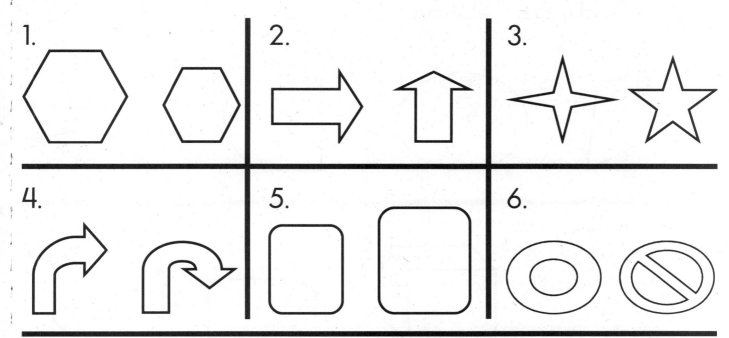

Look at each pair of shapes. Color the shapes that are **congruent**.
Draw an X on the shapes that are **not congruent**.

Name:_____   Date:_____

Review: Symmetry & 3-Dimensional Shapes

Draw a line to show how each shape has **symmetry**.
If you cannot draw a line of **symmetry**, draw an X on the shape.
Color the 3-dimensional shapes.

1.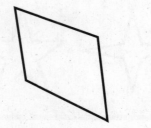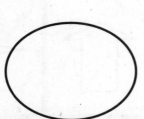

2.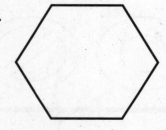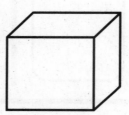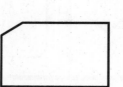

3.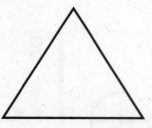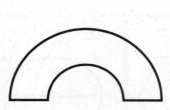

STOP! TAKE A BREAK! You did a great job! Place your Book Mark here & RELAX!

Tip:
Your **line of symmetry** can be horizontal, vertical, or diagonal, or your shape may have more than one type of **symmetry**.

1. Color $\frac{1}{2}$ red.

 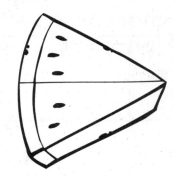 

2. Color $\frac{1}{3}$ green.

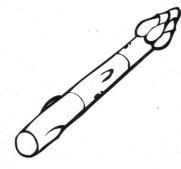 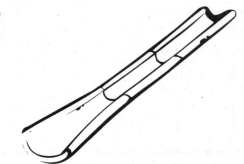 

3. Color $\frac{1}{4}$ orange.

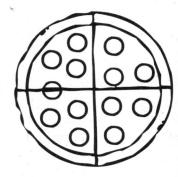 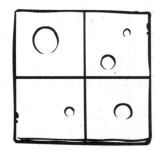 

Circle the **fraction** that describes the shaded portion of each shape.

A.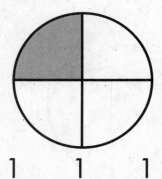

$\frac{1}{2}$ $\frac{1}{3}$ $\frac{1}{4}$

B.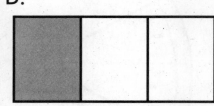

$\frac{1}{2}$ $\frac{1}{3}$ $\frac{1}{4}$

C.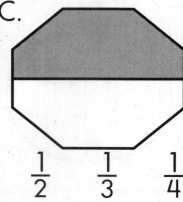

$\frac{1}{2}$ $\frac{1}{3}$ $\frac{1}{4}$

Color the rectangles to show each **fraction**.

D.

$\frac{1}{2}$

E. $\frac{1}{3}$

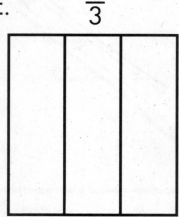

F. $\frac{1}{4}$

G. $\frac{3}{8}$

H. $\frac{1}{8}$

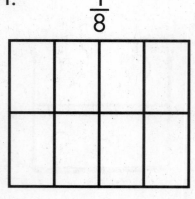

I. $\frac{3}{4}$

Name:_____   Date:_____

Each bug has the same
number of spots.
Count or multiply to find
how many spots in all.

Each one of us has 2 spots!

<u>4</u> ladybugs x <u>2</u> spots on each = 8 spots

Find how many spots by counting or multiplying.

_3_ frogs

x _4_ spots on each

_12_ spots in all

_____ dogs

x _____ spots on each

_____ spots in all

_____ cats

x _____ spots on each

_____ spots in all

_____ mushrooms

x _____ spots on each

_____ spots in all

Name:_____ Date:_____

There are 3 groups of daisies.
There are 5 daisies in each group.
There are 15 daisies in all.

Count or multiply to solve.

A.

2 groups of 4

2 x 4 = ___8___

B.

3 groups of 3

3 x 3 = _____

C.

3 groups of 4

3 x 4 = _____

D.

2 groups of 5

2 x 5 = _____

E.

3 groups of 6

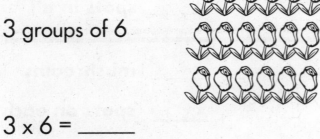

3 x 6 = _____

F.

4 groups of 5

4 x 5 = _____

Understanding the concept of multiplication

Name:_____ Date:_____

How many cherries?
Add or multiply to find out.

4 groups of 3
3 + 3 + 3 + 3 = 12
3 x 4 = 12

Find how many pieces of fruit by adding.
Then, find how many by multiplying.

2 groups of 3   3 + 3 = __6__   2 x 3 = _____

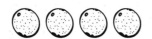 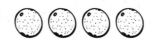 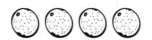 

4 groups of 4   4 + 4 + 4 + 4 = _____   4 x 4 = _____

2 groups of 5   5 + 5 = _____   2 x 5 = _____

3 groups of 3   3 + 3 + 3 = _____   3 x 3 = _____

3 groups of 4   4 + 4 + 4 = _____   3 x 4 = _____

Name:_____ Date:_____

On Monday, 3 bunnies got mail.
Each bunny got 2 letters.
How many letters in all?
3 groups of 2   3 x 2 = 6
6 letters in all

$$\begin{array}{r} 3 \\ \times\,2 \\ \hline 6 \end{array}$$

Read each story problem. Multiply to find the answer.

1. On Tuesday, 3 bunnies got mail.
   Each bunny got 3 letters.
   How many letters in all? _____

2. On Wednesday, 3 bunnies got mail.
   Each bunny got 1 letter.
   How many letters in all? _____

3. On Thursday, 2 bunnies got mail.
   Each bunny got 2 letters.
   How many letters in all? _____

4. On Friday, 2 bunnies got mail.
   Each bunny got 3 letters.
   How many letters in all? _____

5. On Saturday, 1 bunny got mail.
   The bunny got 3 letters.
   How many letters in all? _____

There are 8 strawberries.
Four friends want to share them.
Divide the strawberries among
the friends.
Each friend can have
2 strawberries.

**8 strawberries ÷ 4 friends
= 2 for each friend!**

Divide each set for **2** people to share.

1.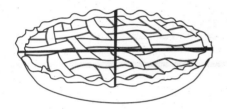

Each person gets _____ piece(s) of pie.

2.

Each person gets _____ can(s) of soda.

3.

Each person gets _____ cupcakes.

Tip:
Draw pictures
and cross out to
help you solve
the problems.

4.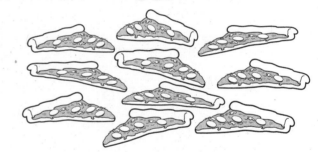

Each person gets _____ slices of pizza.

5.

Each person gets _____ silver stars.

Division is the opposite of multiplication.

$$12 \div 2 = 6 \text{ and } 6 \times 2 = 12$$

Write the division sentence for each multiplication sentence.

A. $4 \times 2 = 8$ _____ $3 \times 3 = 9$ _____

B. $4 \times 5 = 20$ _____ $2 \times 3 = 6$ _____

C. $2 \times 5 = 10$ _____ $3 \times 5 = 15$ _____

Fill in the blanks to make each sentence true.

D. $12 \div 3 = $ _____   _____ $\div 5 = 5$

E. $16 \div $ _____ $= 8$ $18 \div 9 = $ _____

F. _____ $\div 5 = 2$ $12 \div 3 = $ _____

1. Sally and Lisa were making bracelets. There were 8 charms for them to share. How many charms did Sally use?

_____

2. Max and Joe are playing baseball with 10 of their friends. Max and Joe are the captains and will decide on the teams. There has to be the same number of kids on each team. How many kids will be on Max's team, including Max?

_____

Name:_____ Date:_____

Review: Fractions

Color one part. Circle the fraction that names the colored part.

1.

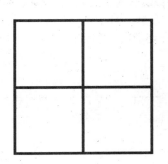

$\dfrac{1}{2}$ $\dfrac{1}{3}$ $\dfrac{1}{4}$

2.

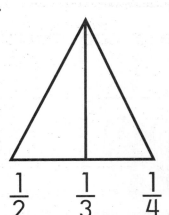

$\dfrac{1}{2}$ $\dfrac{1}{3}$ $\dfrac{1}{4}$

3.

$\dfrac{1}{2}$ $\dfrac{1}{3}$ $\dfrac{1}{4}$

4.

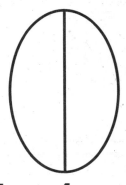

$\dfrac{1}{2}$ $\dfrac{1}{3}$ $\dfrac{1}{4}$

5.

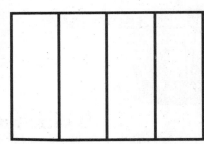

$\dfrac{1}{2}$ $\dfrac{1}{3}$ $\dfrac{1}{4}$

6.

$\dfrac{1}{2}$ $\dfrac{1}{3}$ $\dfrac{1}{4}$

7.

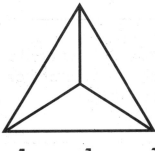

$\dfrac{1}{2}$ $\dfrac{1}{3}$ $\dfrac{1}{4}$

8.

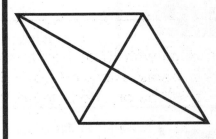

$\dfrac{1}{2}$ $\dfrac{1}{3}$ $\dfrac{1}{4}$

9.

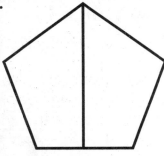

$\dfrac{1}{2}$ $\dfrac{1}{3}$ $\dfrac{1}{4}$

Name:_____ Date:_____

Review: Multiplication & Division

Multiply to find the total number of dots.

A.

__2__ groups of __4__ dots

____ x ____

____ dots in all

B.

____ groups of ____ dots

____ x ____

____ dots in all

C.

____ groups of ____ dots

____ x ____

____ dots in all

Divide to find how many dominoes each person will get.

D.

4 dominoes ÷ 2 people = _____

E.

3 dominoes ÷ 3 people = _____

F.

6 dominoes ÷ 2 people = _____

STOP! TAKE A BREAK! You did a great job! Place your Book Mark here & RELAX!

Answer Key

Please take time to review the work your child or student has completed. Remember to praise both success and effort. If your child makes a mistake, let him or her know that mistakes are a part of learning. Explain why the incorrect response was not the best choice. Then, encourage your child to think it through and select a better choice.

page 3

page 4
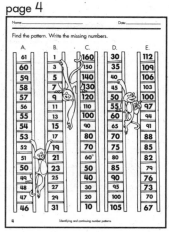

page 5

page 6
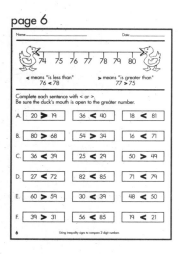

page 7
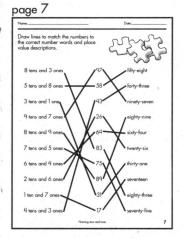

page 8
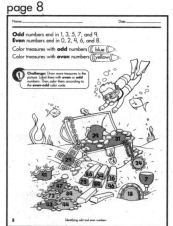

page 9

page 10
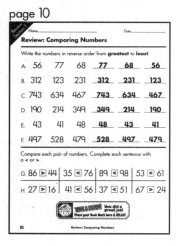

page 11
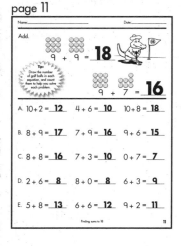

page 12

page 13
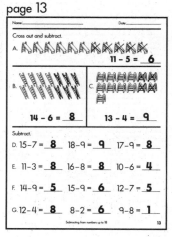

page 14
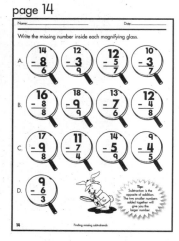

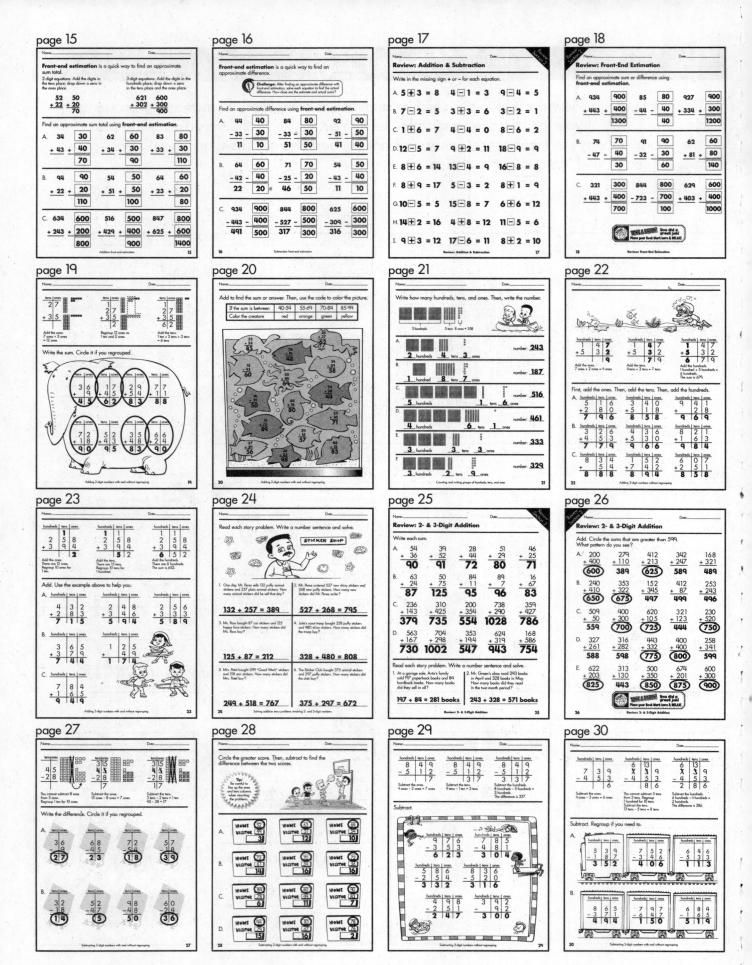

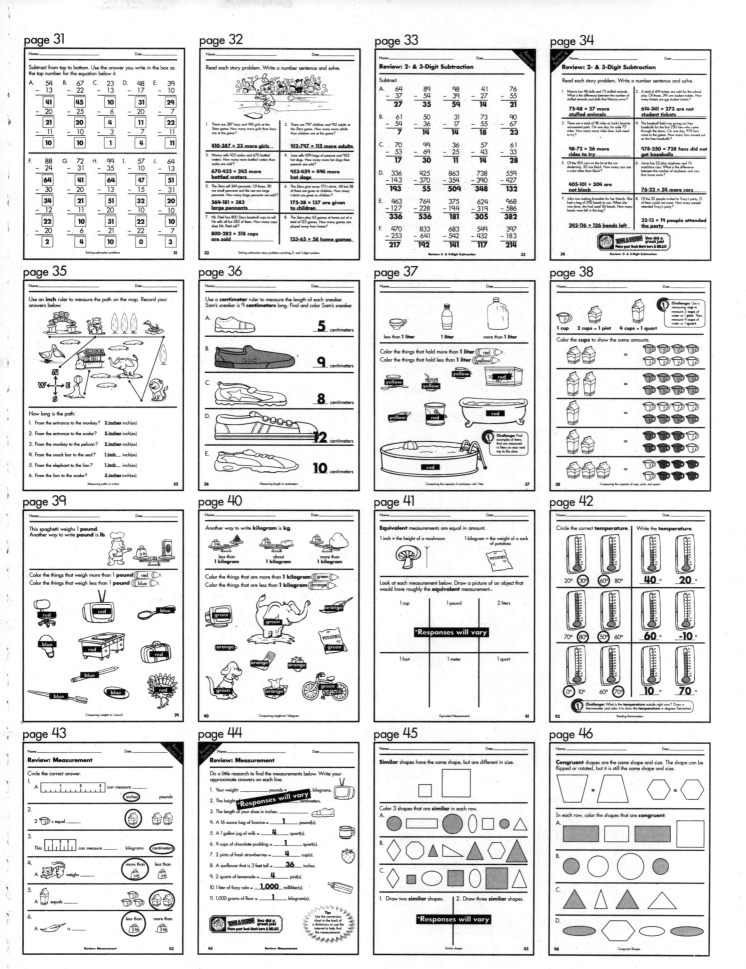

A shape has **symmetry** when a line creates 2 mirror-like halves or sides that are exactly the same.

symmetric   asymmetric

Look at the shapes below. Circle the correct answer.

A. symmetric B. symmetric C. symmetric
D. symmetric E. symmetric F. symmetric

1. Draw a line of **symmetry** on this shape.
2. Draw your own shape that is symmetric.

Responses will vary

Line of Symmetry   47

cube   cone   cylinder   sphere

1. Write down 3 things that have the same shape as a **cube**.
   1. a box
   2. playing dice
   3. ice cube

Challenge: Find some scrap paper and a roll of tape. Can you fold, bend, roll, or twist the paper to form a **cube**? How about a **cone**? Try making a **cylinder** or **sphere** with paper, too!

2. Write the name of 6 different sports where a ball shaped like a **sphere** is used.
   1. basketball   4. baseball
   2. soccer   5. golf
   3. volleyball   6.

3. Draw a picture of 3 food products that might be found in a can shaped like a **cylinder**. **Responses will vary**
   soup   pop   tuna   vegetables

4. Draw a picture of 2 things that have the same shape as a **cone**.
   ice cream cone   construction cone   party hat

48   Three-Dimensional Shapes

Review: Similar & Congruent Shapes

Look at each pair of shapes. Color the shapes that are **similar**. Draw an X on the box if the shapes are **not similar**.

Look at each pair of shapes. Color the shapes that are **congruent**. Draw an X on the shapes. That are **not congruent**.

Review: Similar & Congruent Shapes   49

Review: Symmetry & 3-Dimensional Shapes

Draw a line to show how each shape has **symmetry**. If you cannot draw a line of **symmetry**, draw an X on the shape.

Responses will vary. Other options may be correct.

Tip: Your **line of symmetry** may be horizontal, vertical, or diagonal, or your shape may have more than one type of symmetry.

50   Review: Symmetry & 3-Dimensional Shapes

1. Color $\frac{1}{2}$ red.
2. Color $\frac{1}{3}$ green.
3. Color $\frac{1}{4}$ orange.

Recognizing halves, thirds, and fourths   51

Circle the **fraction** that describes the shaded portion of each shape.

A. $\frac{1}{2}$ B. $\frac{1}{4}$ C. $\frac{1}{2}$

Color the rectangles to show each **fraction**.

D. $\frac{1}{2}$ E. $\frac{1}{3}$ F. $\frac{1}{4}$

G. $\frac{3}{8}$ H. $\frac{1}{8}$ I. $\frac{3}{4}$

52   Fractions

Each bug has the same number of spots. Count or multiply to find how many spots in all.

4 ladybugs x 2 spots on each = 8 spots

Find how many spots by counting or multiplying.

3 frogs x 4 spots on each = 12 spots in all
2 dogs x 6 spots on each = 12 spots in all
4 cats x 5 spots on each = 20 spots in all
4 mushrooms x 4 spots on each = 16 spots in all

Combining equal groups   53

There are 3 groups of daisies.
There are 5 daisies in each group.
There are 15 daisies in all.

Count or multiply to solve.

A. 2 groups of 4   2 x 4 = 8
B. 3 groups of 3   3 x 3 = 9
C. 3 groups of 4   3 x 4 = 12
D. 2 groups of 5   2 x 5 = 10
E. 3 groups of 6   3 x 6 = 18
F. 4 groups of 5   4 x 5 = 20

54   Understanding the concept of multiplication

How many cherries? Add or multiply to find out.
4 groups of 3
3 + 3 + 3 + 3 = 12
3 x 4 = 12

Find how many pieces of fruit by adding. Then, find how many by multiplying.

2 groups of 3   3 + 3 = 6   2 x 3 = 6
4 groups of 4   4 + 4 + 4 + 4 = 16   4 x 4 = 16
2 groups of 5   5 + 5 = 10   2 x 5 = 10
3 groups of 3   3 + 3 + 3 = 9   3 x 3 = 9
3 groups of 4   4 + 4 + 4 = 12   3 x 4 = 12

Relating repeated addition and multiplication   55

Remember with equal groups you can multiply.

On Monday, 3 bunnies got mail.
Each bunny got 2 letters.
How many letters in all?
3 groups of 2   3 x 2 = 6
6 letters in all

Read each story problem. Multiply to find the answer.

1. On Tuesday, 3 bunnies got mail.
   Each bunny got 3 letters.
   How many letters in all?   9
2. On Wednesday, 3 bunnies got mail.
   Each bunny got 1 letter.
   How many letters in all?   3
3. On Thursday, 2 bunnies got mail.
   Each bunny got 2 letters.
   How many letters in all?   4
4. On Friday, 2 bunnies got mail.
   Each bunny got 3 letters.
   How many letters in all?   6
5. On Saturday, 1 bunny got mail.
   The bunny got 3 letters.
   How many letters in all?   3

56   Multiplying by 1, 2, and 3

There are 8 strawberries.
Four friends want to share them.
Divide the strawberries among the friends.
Each friend can have 2 strawberries.

8 strawberries ÷ 4 friends = 2 for each friend!

Divide each set for **2** people to share.

1. Each person gets 2 piece(s) of pie.
2. Each person gets 1 can(s) of soda.
3. Each person gets 4 cupcakes.
4. Each person gets 5 slices of pizza.
5. Each person gets 4 silver stars.

Understanding the concept of division   57

Division is the opposite of multiplication.

$12 ÷ 2 = 6$ and $6 × 2 = 12$

Write the division sentence for each multiplication sentence.

A. 4 x 2 = 8   8 ÷ 4 = 2 or 8 ÷ 2 = 4   3 x 3 = 9   9 ÷ 3 = 3
B. 4 x 5 = 20   20 ÷ 5 = 4 or 20 ÷ 4 = 5   3 x 2 = 6   6 ÷ 3 = 2 or 6 ÷ 2 = 3
C. 2 x 5 = 10   10 ÷ 5 = 2 or 10 ÷ 2 = 5   3 x 5 = 15   15 ÷ 5 = 3 or 15 ÷ 3 = 5

Fill in the blanks to make each sentence true.

D. 12 ÷ 3 = 4   25 ÷ 5 = 5
E. 16 ÷ 2 = 8   18 ÷ 9 = 2
F. 10 ÷ 5 = 2   12 ÷ 3 = 4

1. Sally and Lisa were making bracelets. There were 8 charms for them to share. How many charms did Sally use?
   Sally used 4 charms.

2. Max and Joe are playing baseball with 10 of their friends. Max and Joe are the captains and will decide on the teams. There has to be the same number of kids on each team. How many kids will be on Max's team, including Max?
   There are 6 kids on the team, including Max.

58   Understanding the concept of division

Review: Fractions

Color one part. Circle the fraction that names the colored part.

1. $\frac{1}{2}$ $\frac{1}{4}$
2. $\frac{1}{3}$ $\frac{1}{4}$
3. $\frac{1}{2}$ $\frac{1}{4}$
4. $\frac{1}{2}$ $\frac{1}{4}$
5. $\frac{1}{3}$ $\frac{1}{4}$
6. $\frac{1}{3}$ $\frac{1}{4}$
7. $\frac{1}{2}$ $\frac{1}{4}$
8. $\frac{1}{2}$ $\frac{1}{4}$
9. $\frac{1}{2}$ $\frac{1}{4}$

Review: Fractions   59

Review: Multiplication & Division

Multiply to find the total number of dots.

A. 2 groups of 4 dots   2 x 4 = 8 dots in all
B. 2 groups of 2 dots   2 x 2 = 4 dots in all
C. 2 groups of 8 dots   2 x 8 = 16 dots in all

Divide to find how many dominoes each person will get.

D. 4 dominoes ÷ 2 people = 2
E. 3 dominoes ÷ 3 people = 1
F. 6 dominoes ÷ 2 people = 3

60   Review: Multiplication & Division

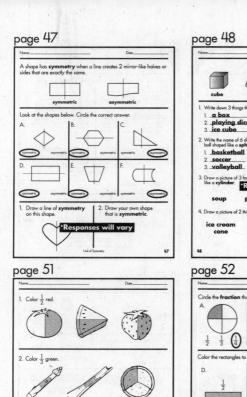
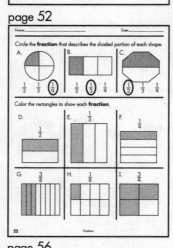

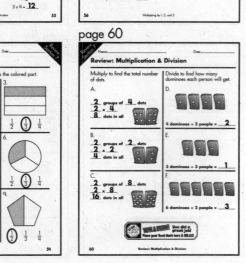
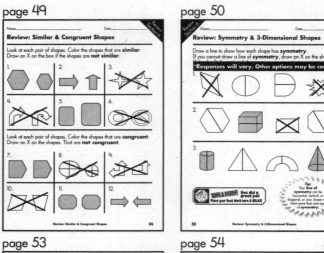
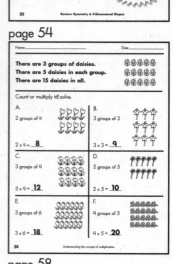
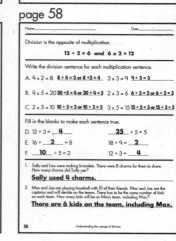
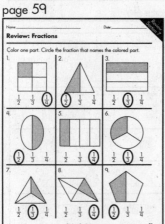

ADDITION BINGO

1. Cut out the game boards & find some chips, paper scraps, or pennies to use as your game board markers.
2. Have a friend or family member call out an addition sentence from the purple board. Find the matching answer on the blue board and cover it with a game board marker.
3. Then switch and have the caller call out an answer from the blue board - find a matching addition sentence on the purple board and cover it with a game board marker.
4. How quickly can you cover 4 in a row or the whole board?

⚽	3+7=	9+10=	8+7=
5+4=	7+5=	4+3=	8+6=
7+6=	4+2=	7+9=	9+8=
2+9=	2+3=	10+10=	🏈

CUT HERE

11	13	10	7
9	15	🐕	12
20	16	5	14
🐕	19	17	6

AWESOME WORK!!

YOUR MATH SKILLS ARE HUGE!

Take a break & come back to have more fun with numbers!

_____'s

(Your Name)

YOUR SKILLS are HOT!

Check off these skills as you practice them in the book:

- Place Values
- Evens & Odds
- Front-end Estimation

- 2-Digit & 3-Digit Addition
- 2-Digit & 3-Digit Subtraction
- Word Problems

- Inches & Centimeters
- Cups, Pints & Quarts
- Pounds & Kilograms
- Temperature
- Converting Measurements

- Similar & Congruent Shapes
- Symmetry
- 3-Dimensional Shapes

- Fractions
- Multiplication
- Division

SUBTRACTION BINGO

1. Cut out the game boards & get several bingo markers (e.g. paper scraps, pennies, candy, or cereal pieces).
2. Ask a friend to call out a subtraction sentence from the red board. You find the correct answer on the orange board and cover it with a bingo marker.
3. Continue play until you have 4 in a row – that's BINGO!
4. Alternative play: Have your friend call out an answer from the orange board while you find the matching subtraction sentence on the red board.

12-8=	16-8=	14-5=	11-6=
8-6=	20-6=	13-7=	18-5=
	12-5=	15-3=	20-4=
19-9=	17-6=	19-4=	

CUT HERE

16	11	5	9
2		7	12
13	8	15	10
4	6	14	